WriteTraits®
STUDENT TRAITBOOK

Vicki Spandel • Jeff Hicks

GReaT SOuRCe®
EDUCATION GROUP
A Houghton Mifflin Company

Vicki Spandel

Vicki Spandel was codirector of the original teacher team that developed the six-trait model and has designed instructional materials for all grade levels. She has written several books, including *Creating Writers–Linking Writing Assessment and Instruction* (Longman), and is a former language arts teacher, journalist, technical writer, consultant, and scoring director for dozens of state, county, and district writing assessments.

Jeff Hicks

Jeff Hicks has over 17 years of teaching experience in grades two through nine. Until recently, Jeff taught seventh/eighth grade English and math on a two-person teaching team, focusing on the reading/writing connection through six-trait writing activities. Currently, Jeff is a full-time writer and presenter.

Design/Production: Bill Westwood/Andy Cox, David Drury

Illustration: Jim Higgins, Mark DaGrossa, Scott Van Buren, Chris Vallo

Proofreading/Editorial: Erik Martin/Judy Bernheim, Alex Culpepper

Cover: Illustration by Claude Martinot Design

Printed in the United States of America

International Standard Book Number: 0-669-50475-0

1 2 3 4 5 6 7 8 9 10 – BA – 07 06 05 04 03

Contents

Unit 1: Ideas

Unit 2: Organization

Unit 3: Voice

Unit 4: Word Choice

Unit 5: Sentence Fluency

Unit 6: Conventions

Warm-up Activity

What Changed?

Read...

Sometimes, writers think of another way to say something. Then, they make changes in their writing. Changing your writing is called **revising**.

Read two stories about Ben and his cat. See what kinds of changes the writer made.

Sample 1

Ben and His Cat (I)

Ben did not want to go to the store with his mom. He wanted to stay home to play with his cat. He went anyway. At the store, Ben got a treat for himself and for his cat. Then, Ben and his mom went home.

Think...

Did you like the story? Write your ideas here:

_____

_____

_____

Sample 2

Ben and His Cat (2)

Ben was not happy. His mom told him he had to go to the store with her. Ben did not want to go! He hated those huge grocery carts, whizzing around the corners, almost crashing into him. He wanted to stay home and play with his cat Chloe. He liked to pretend she was a tiger stalking him through the jungle of his bedroom. But his mom said, "Don't worry. We'll find a surprise—something extra yummy." Sure enough, when they got to the store, Ben got a treat. His mom bought him an ice cream cone! They even bought a can of tuna for Chloe. Ben could already picture Chloe licking her whiskers when he got home and fed her the tuna. He was glad he had come!

Think...

Did you like this story? Is it better than the first one? Write your ideas here:

_____

_____

_____

Unit 1
Ideas

Do you know your head has many ideas? That's right! Ideas are all the things you think about. Ideas come from all the things you see or hear or smell or taste or feel. Now, all you have to do is get your ideas on paper.

The Word and Picture Team

Think about a fat, gray squirrel with a bushy tail. He is running up a tree to get away from a huge, yellow dog. Can you see the squirrel and the dog in your mind? Could you draw a picture of them? Sure! Words make pictures in a reader's mind. Pictures help writers think of good words to use. Words and pictures make a team.

Read

Good writers use words to make pictures in our minds. Read about a girl and her dog, Flag. In the story, Flag gets lost in the desert. What pictures do you see in your mind?

Before bed I got out my photos of Flag. I couldn't help crying. But I laughed some too.

The picture of Flag catching lima beans was my favorite. That was Flag's best trick. I hate lima beans, so Flag got mine. Every time I threw one in the air, he would catch it. Once he caught sixteen in a row!

Paul Brett Johnson and Celeste Lewis. *Lost.* (New York: Scholastic, 1996).

Think

Think hard about what you just read. What did you see in your mind? Share your ideas with your class.

Draw

Flag is very good at catching lima beans! Do you have a pet or a favorite animal that is good at something? Think hard. Try to see the animal in your mind. Now, draw what you see.

Write

Look carefully at your picture on page 3. Write something important about your animal.

_____

_____

_____

_____

_____

_____

_____

_____

Share

Share your writing with a friend. Be a good listener when it is your friend's turn to share.

Scribbles Has a Question

"Help! I can't get my writing started. I don't have any good ideas."

Scribbles is a writer, like you. Today, he is having trouble. What should we tell Scribbles?

HINT: Think about how writers use pictures.

A Writer's Secret

Good writers know secrets to make their writing easy to read. One writer's secret is using capital letters. A capital letter can tell the reader a new sentence is starting.

Scribbles wrote about his dog. But it looks like he forgot an important writer's secret. Can you help?

bonzo is my dog. she is the biggest dog I have ever seen. i think she is bigger than Clifford.

name: .... date: ....

What's the BIG Idea?

What holds your burrito together? If you said "the tortilla," you are right! The tortilla wraps around the filling. It hugs the meat and beans and cheese so nothing can fall out. Good writing is like a burrito. It needs one big idea to hold all the little ideas together. The big idea, called the main idea, is like the tortilla.

Read

What is the author's main idea?

Polar bears have the biggest feet of all eight bear species. Their huge, padded feet are extra-wide—kind of like snowshoes that help them walk in the snow without sinking in. The bottoms of their feet are even covered with hairy non-skid surface to keep them from slipping on the ice.

Lisa McCourt. *Hairy 'N' Weird (the strangest mammals you ever saw)*. (Lincolnwood, IL: Lowell House, 2000)

Think

Did this author have a main idea? What held these sentences together? Look at this list of main ideas. Put an X by the one you think is the main idea.

_____ Bears

_____ Snowshoes

_____ Polar bear feet

_____ Ice

Read Again

Does this writer have a main idea? Write your answer on the lines below.

  I like to ride my bike over the curb to get some air. Cheddar cheese is good on hamburgers. Canada geese fly in the shape of a big "V."

_____

_____

Share

Share your answer with a partner. Do you agree?

Write

The last writer did not have a clear main idea. The writing went from bike riding to cheese to geese. That was hard to follow.

You can do better! First, choose a main idea. Choose one of these or pick one of your own. Put a check by the idea you pick.

_____ Swimming

_____ Something I love to do

_____ Spiders

_____ My own idea _____

Now, write about your main idea here. Write at least 3 sentences.

_____

_____

_____

_____

_____

Read your 3 sentences. Did you stick to your main idea?

_____ Yes!   _____ No

Share

Be ready to share your writing out loud. Listen for the main idea as each person reads.

Scribbles Has a Question

"I don't have a main idea. I write whatever comes into my head! Is this OK?"

What do you think? What will you tell Scribbles?

A Writer's Secret

A good writer's secret is to make sure every sentence ends with the right punctuation mark. Most sentences end with periods. Some end with question marks.

It looks like Scribbles forgot this writer's secret. Can you help?

I love winter I love to play in the snow When I come in,

I drink hot chocolate

name: .... date: ....

Wanted: Good Details!

What if your pet was lost? You might make a poster. Then, people could help find your pet. If you said, "She's kind of big," would it help? Probably not! It would help if you said, "Fuzzy is a big, round, yellow cat with long hair and white feet. She has large, pointy ears and a fat tail." Details give information. Details make the picture clear.

Read

Read a short passage about a knight. We have written it three ways. One is the way the author really wrote it.

HINT: It's the one with the best details!

_____ 1. We looked at the Black Knight. He was dressed in black.

_____ 2. We looked at the Black Knight. He had on shoes, pants, and other things.

_____ 3. We looked at the Black Knight. He had on pointed metal shoes, armored pants, an armored coat with hinges at the elbows and shoulders, and a huge metal helmet that looked like a black bell, all topped off with a fluffy black feather.

Jon Scieszka. *The Time Warp Trio: Knights of the Kitchen Table.* (New York: Puffin Books, 1993), p. 5.

Think

Which one (1, 2, or 3) makes the best picture in your mind? Which one has the best details? Put a check by that one.

Think Again

Read Number 3 again. What details did the author give us to make a clear picture?

Details

_____

_____

_____

_____

_____

Write

Read these sentences about a favorite tree:

My favorite climbing tree is big. It has bark.
My tree has branches.

Can you see the tree in your mind? You could see it better if the writer used more details. Pick one of these sentences. Add details to help a reader picture the tree.

_____

_____

_____

_____

_____

Share

Share your new sentence. Listen while others share their sentences, too. Do the details help you see the tree in your mind?

Scribbles Has a Question

"I want to write about my dog. I need details. Ask me questions to help me think of some details."

Write a question that would help Scribbles "think details."

_____

_____

A Writer's Secret

The words *to*, *two*, and *too* all sound the same. But they do not mean the same thing! You need to choose the right one. Otherwise, your words won't make sense.

Did Scribbles use the right words here? Can you fix them?

I have <u>to</u> dogs. I took them <u>too</u> see the vet.

name: .... date: ....

Sticking with It

There are so many things to write about. You could write about a pet, a loose tooth, or a ride on a roller coaster. What if you wrote about all those things in one paper? Your readers could get confused! Good writers stick to one topic. They don't wander.

Main topic

Read

Read the two samples of writing. Do the writers stick to their topics? Or do they wander?

Sample 1

Going to my grandma and grandpa's farm is fun. They have horses, cows, and a big house. They have pigs, too. I am good at math. I have two cats and a turtle. My Aunt Sue likes to fish.

This writer

_____ stayed on topic.

_____ wandered.

Sample 2

We had a Science Fair at my school. My friend Nico and I did a project about bubbles. We called it "Bubblemania." We made a bubble solution of soap and water. Then we added some corn syrup. The syrup made our bubbles bigger. It made them last a long, long time.

This writer

_____ stayed on topic.

_____ wandered.

Think

Look back at Sample 1. Underline the parts that wander.

Share

Be ready to share what you underlined. Why did you underline those parts?

Think

It's time to write. First, choose a topic. Choose an idea from the list or think of your own. Put a check by the idea you pick.

Topics

____ Riding a bike

____ Snakes

____ A loose tooth

____ My own idea _____

Write

Write at least 3 sentences. Tell something interesting or important about your topic. Remember, don't wander!

_____

_____

_____

_____

_____

Share

Share your writing with a friend. Listen as you each read your writing out loud. Put a star by any place you wander.

Scribbles Has a Question

"Boy, did I have a busy weekend! I will write about my new shoes, my trip to the zoo, and catching snakes. What do you think?"

What advice would you give Scribbles?

_____

_____

_____

A Writer's Secret

Always check your spelling. If you spell a word wrong, it could change your message. Scribbles wrote, I lick snakes. He meant to say, I like snakes.

A word is spelled wrong in this sentence, too. Can you find it? Can you fix it?

It is time to leave four school.

Organization

Which do you put on first, your socks or your shoes? Things need to go in order, don't they? That's called **organization**. Good organization can help you keep your desk neat or your room picked up. It can also help your writing make sense. The next four lessons will help you do that.

name: .... date: ....

Just like a Puzzle

Writing is like putting a puzzle together. Every piece has to fit just right. When you write, you need to put all your ideas in the right places, too. Organized ideas make a clear picture for your reader.

Read

Read this short piece of writing. Think of every sentence like a piece in a puzzle. Do the pieces fit? Do they make a clear picture? Does the writing make sense?

Sample 1

We got there just fine, and now I love flying. That made me nervous! I was so glad! The car ride takes forever. I wasn't worried until the wind made our plane bump up and down! This year we decided to fly. Flying would be so much faster. Every December we go to my grandparent's house.

Think

What do you think of the writer's organization? Were the ideas in the right places? Mark your choice with an X.

___ This writing makes sense. The sentences are in order.

___ This does not make sense! The sentences are out of order.

Read Again

Now, the sentences are in a different order. Does the writing make sense?

Sample 2

Every December we go to my grandparent's house. This year we decided to fly. I was so glad! The car ride takes forever. Flying would be so much faster. I wasn't worried until the wind made our plane bump up and down. That made me nervous! We got there just fine, and now I love flying.

Think

How did it sound this time? Did the writer get the details in the right order? Mark your choice with an X.

___ This is much better. It makes sense now.

___ It was better the first time.

Read

This recipe has five steps. Some are out of order. Number them in order.

HINT: Read out loud as you work. It helps!

Ants on a Log

___ Enjoy your tasty snack!

___ Spread some peanut butter on top of each celery "log."

___ Put your "ants on a log" on a small plate.

___ With an adult's help, cut some celery into six pieces.

___ Place raisin "ants" in the peanut butter on top of your celery "log."

Share

When you are done, read your recipe out loud to yourself. Does it make sense?

___ Yes. The 5 steps are all in order!

___ No! It still does not make sense.

If you said no, try again!

Scribbles Has a Question

"Why is order a big deal? If I have lots of ideas, can't I write them in any order?"

Think about the recipe you worked on. Now, write a note to Scribbles.

_____

_____

A Writer's Secret

Some sentences are questions. They need to end with question marks.

Oops! Maybe Scribbles needs your help with this writer's secret.

Do you like Ants on a Log I really do.

What is your favorite food

Lesson 6

name: .... date: ....

Starting Off with a Bang!

Have you ever gone up a steep hill? Or raced with your friends? Then, you know it's important to get off to a good start. Writers need a good start, too. A strong beginning, or lead, pulls your readers into your writing. It makes them want to keep reading!

Read

Do you like books? If you do, you might already have a good eye and ear for interesting leads. Maybe you know that a good lead can

- get your attention
- give you the shivers!
- make you wonder what will happen
- make you want to keep reading!

Here are four leads. Read them. Then, mark how you feel about each one.

Lead #1

When Eddie Dickens was eleven years old, both his parents caught some awful disease that made them turn yellow, go a bit crinkly around the edges, and smell of old hot-water bottles.

Philip Ardagh, *A House Called Awful End* (New York: Holt, 2000) p. 3

Would you like to read more?

___ Yes!   ___ No, not really.

Lead #2

There are fun things you can do on a bike. Bikes are fun. Bikes are neat.

Would you like to read more?

___ Yes!   ___ No, not really.

Lead #3

Deer are really cool. They eat, run, and play.

Would you like to read more?

___ Yes!   ___ No, not really.

Lead #4

They didn't call it Energy Hill for nothing! I had only gone five steps and I was panting! I could not even breathe. That hill went straight up into the sky. I needed to rest, but I did not want the other kids to make fun of me. So I pretended to tie my shoes.

Would you like to read more?

___ Yes!   ___ No, not really.

Think and Share

Finish this sentence.

A good lead _____

_____

_____

Write

Remember, a good lead makes you want to read more. Pick one of these topics or make up your own. Write a lead that will make your reader want to keep reading!

____ Bikes

____ Climbing

____ A person I like

____ My own topic:

_____

For my lead, I would write this:

_____

_____

_____

Share

Read your lead out loud to yourself. Will your reader want to keep reading?

Scribbles Has a Question

"I want to write about the day I learned to roller skate. It was awesome! But I don't know how to begin."

How can Scribbles start his story off with a bang?

A Writer's Secret

Sometimes writers write so fast they run their words together such as: likethis. This makes writing hard to read. How can you remember to put in spaces? The secret is to <u>look again</u>.

Scribbles forgot to look over his writing. Does he need more spaces? Can you show him where?
Use this mark: #

How was theplane going to get offthe ground?

It looked waytoo heavy.

One Story at a Time!

You might want to write about a roller coaster ride. What a great idea! You could also write about making a birdhouse. That's a great idea, too! It's not a good idea to write about both in the same story. Be organized. Tell one story at a time.

Read

Read this short piece of writing. Is this writer telling one story? Or two stories?

My Pirate Birthday Party

I am going to be seven on my birthday. I am having the best birthday party ever. It is a pirate party with eye patches and a treasure hunt. I will have a cake decorated like a treasure map. My dog is named Cody. He is four. He can jump fences. Cody will eat just about any kind of food. He even eats peaches!

Think

Did this person write about one thing? Or two things? Let's see.

Here are all the sentences from "My Pirate Birthday Party" in a list. Get a red crayon and a blue crayon. Then, put a **red X** by every sentence that is about the pirate birthday party. Put a **blue X** by every sentence that is about something else.

My Pirate Birthday Party

_____ I am going to be seven on my birthday.

_____ I am having the best birthday party ever.

_____ It is a pirate party with eye patches and a treasure hunt.

_____ I will have a cake decorated like a treasure map.

_____ My dog is named Cody.

_____ He is four.

_____ He can jump fences.

_____ Cody will eat just about any kind of food.

_____ He even eats peaches!

Think & Pick

Now, it's your turn to be the writer. Tell only one story. Choose an idea from the list below or think of your own.

Topics

___ A great birthday party

___ My favorite dessert

___ A funny pet

___ My own idea

My topic will be _____

_____.

Write

Write at least three sentences. Tell something interesting or important about your topic. Don't wander! Stay on one topic.

_____

_____

_____

Share

Share your writing with a partner. Listen carefully to each other. Did you stick to your topic? Put a red star above your writing if you did.

Scribbles Has a Question

One thing at a time.

"I want to tell about going to the beach! I also want to write about being in a storm. Can I put both things in one paper?"

What should Scribbles do?

_____

_____

A Writer's Secret

Write your title last. Then, you can be sure your title will fit your paper. What is a good title for Scribbles' paper?

At my secret place, you can make giant sand castles. Then you can watch the waves melt them! Can you guess what my secret place is? I will give you one more clue. You might see a fish there.

The Finish Line

name: .... date: ....

Most people do not stop watching a TV show or movie right in the middle. If you did that, you would not know the ending. Good endings are important. A good ending is not just the place where the writing stops. A good ending finishes the writing.

Read

Authors finish their writing in lots of ways. A good ending might

- solve a mystery
- answer a question
- tell something important the writer learned
- surprise you!
- make you wish the writer would keep going!
- or _____ (Write in your own idea.)

Read these two endings. Then, mark how you feel with an **X**.

Ending #1

This is the end of my story. I don't know what else to say.

Do you like this ending?

____ Yes, it's great!

____ No, not really.

Ending #2

Uncle Wolf didn't have chicken stew that night, but Mrs. Chicken fixed him a nice dinner anyway.

"Aw, shucks," he thought, as he walked home, "maybe tomorrow I'll bake the little critters a hundred scrumptious cookies!"

Keiko Kasza, *The Wolf's Chicken Stew* (New York: Sandcastle Books, 1987).

Do you like this ending?

____ Yes, it makes me wonder what happened in the story.

____ No, not really.

Read and Choose

Here are three possible endings to a story about a girl named Alli and her horse, Sonny. Sonny broke his leg, but now he is better and he wants to run. Which one finishes the story best? Circle A, B, or C to show your favorite.

A

Now that her horse's leg had finally healed, Alli knew he couldn't wait to get out of the barn. She had barely pushed the big door open when Sonny took off across the field. His swift feet hardly touched the ground.

B

Alli's horse, Sonny, had broken his leg. Now it was better, so that's the end of my story.

C

So now you know all about Alli and Sonny. The End.

Write

This piece of writing needs an ending. Read the story carefully. Then, write an ending you think a reader will like.

Finally, the snow began to fall. Even though it was dark out, Jaimie could tell the snow was sticking. Would it stop or keep snowing? She stared out her bedroom window at the big flakes. "Please stick," she kept whispering. Her eyes got very heavy. At last, she could not keep them open any longer. Jaimie fell asleep dreaming of snow.

Finish this story. Write your ending here:

_____

_____

_____

Scribbles Has a Question

"When I come to the end of my story, can't I just say, 'The End'?"

What would you tell Scribbles?

_____

_____

_____

A Writer's Secret

Whenever you talk about yourself in writing, use a capital "I." Use capital "I" even in the middle of a sentence. Then, your readers will always know that it's you!

Scribbles hasn't learned this secret yet. Can you help?

i didn't know what to do. If only i hadn't followed them. i should have listened to my parents.

Unit 3
Voice

When a friend calls you on the phone, can you tell who it is? Sure! Every friend has a different voice. Every writer has a different voice, too. In the next four lessons, you will have a chance to hear different voices, think about voice, and try out your own voice. Voice makes your writing different and special.

name: ....   date: ....

An Ear for Voice

Do you have a favorite book or story? What makes it your favorite? Maybe it's the writer's voice. Voice is the way a writer speaks to us.

Read

Writers with strong voices make us feel things. They might make us laugh or cry or feel scared. Read three short samples of writing. Do you like what you hear? Do you want to hear more? Put an **X** in the right blank to show your feelings.

Voice makes us feel things.

Sample 1

Dragon slaying, thought Wiglaf. It sounded pretty gruesome. But dragons were evil. They deserved to be slain—didn't they? And who slew them? Mighty heroes, that's who!

Maps tacked to the tree showed the way from Pinwick to Dragon Slayer's Academy. Wiglaf pulled one off and stared at it. Here was a path he might follow to become a hero!

K. H. McMullan. *Dragon Slayer's Academy*, *1*, "The New Kid At School." (New York: Grosset & Dunlap, 1997).

____ I liked it! Let's hear some more!

____ I didn't like it. I've heard enough.

Sample 2

Skateboarding is fun. I have fun when I skateboard. It is fun to do tricks. My friends like it, too. We have fun when we skateboard.

____ I liked it! Let's hear some more!

____ I didn't like it. I've heard enough.

Sample 3

I am a dog person. I don't mean that I am a talking dog or a person who was changed into a dog by magic. I mean, I *like* dogs! My brother is a cat person, so he has a cat named Jinglebell. (Yes, he got her for Christmas.) I have a dog named Tank. She's a pug. Tank and Jinglebell get along just fine. It's my brother and I who fight like cats and dogs!

____ I liked it! Let's hear some more!

____ I didn't like it. I've heard enough.

Share with a Partner

Share how you felt about each sample with a friend. See if you agree or not. Be a good listener when it is your friend's turn to share. It's OK if you do not always agree.

Write

Write what voice means to you. Think about the samples you liked and why you liked them.

_____

_____

_____

_____

_____

_____

Scribbles Has a Question

"I like the color red and the color purple! Can colors have voice? What about food? I love pizza! I love chocolate, too. Can food have voice?"

What do you think about Scribbles' questions?

A Writer's Secret

Writers sometimes use exclamation marks to show excitement or strong feelings.

Scribbles wrote about how much he likes candy. Could an exclamation point help show his strong feelings? Pick one of his sentences and change the period to an exclamation point.

I love candy. Candy is the best thing in the whole world.

name: .... date: ....

A Bouquet of Voices

Have you ever seen a balloon bouquet (bō-KAY)? Maybe the balloons were all different colors. That makes a bouquet more interesting. There are all kinds of voices in writing, too. They can be happy, sad, excited, or quiet. Different voices make writing interesting. In this lesson, you'll hear some great voices and think of some words to describe each one.

silly
bouncy
shy
sad
happy
smart
puzzled
crazy
quiet
funny

Read

Read three short pieces of writing. Each one is filled with voice, but every voice is different. Think of some words to describe each voice. Write the words in the balloons.

Voice 1

Mr. Twit felt that this hairiness made him look terrifically wise and grand. But in truth he was neither of these things. Mr. Twit was a twit. He was born a twit. And now at the age of sixty, he was a bigger twit than ever.

The hair on Mr. Twit's face didn't grow smooth and matted as it does on most hairy-faced men. It grew in spikes that stuck out straight like the bristles of a nailbrush.

And how often did Mr. Twit wash this bristly nailbrushy face of his?

The answer is NEVER, not even on Sundays.

Roald Dahl. *The Twits* (New York: Scholastic, 1980), pp. 3–5.

What are some words to describe this voice?

_____ _____ _____

Voice 2

Miguel looks down at his cereal. Today he has gotten the blue bowl. He is sorry that he has made Tia Lola feel unwelcomed. He knows what that feels like. At school, an older kid in his class named Mort has nicknamed him Gooseman, because that's what Miguel's last name, Guzman, sounds like in English. Now other kids are calling out, "Quack, quack!" whenever they pass him in the hall. Maybe they are trying to be funny, but it makes him feel embarrassed and unwelcomed.

Julia Alvarez. *How Tia Lola Came to Stay* (New York: Dell, 2001) pp. 22–23.

What are some words to describe this voice?

_____   _____   _____

Voice 3

Spotted Moray

I often stop and play with morays. I've even hugged a few! Moray eels can be dangerous, though, if you happen to be a small fish or octopus. Watch out! You could become an eel meal! But people aren't on their menu. In fact, these gentle and curious fish remind me of kittens. It's easy to see why this one is called a spotted moray, a fine name for a totally freckled fish.

Sylvia A. *Earle. Hello Fish! Visiting The Coral Reef.* Washington, D.C.: National Geographic, 1999).

What are some words to describe this voice?

_____   _____   _____

Scribbles Has a Question

"I can only think of two kinds of voices—happy and sad. That's like chocolate and vanilla ice cream. Are two flavors enough?"

Look back at some of the words in the balloon bouquet. Does voice come in more than two flavors? Is that a good thing?

A Writer's Secret

Many words sound the same but are spelled differently. They also have different meanings.

| to, too, two | wait, weight | here, hear |
| for, four | night, knight | write, right |

Using the wrong word can change the meaning of your ideas. Fix this sentence.

The last **knight** of vacation is almost **hear**.

name: _____ date: _____

Hear Me Roar!

If you want someone to hear your speaking voice, you speak. If you want someone to hear your singing voice, you sing! You also have a writing voice. How can you let it be heard? By writing and drawing! In this lesson, you will write and draw. So, let your writer's voice roar!

Think, Know, Care, Choose!

Today, you choose what you want to write about. If you pick something you know a lot about, your writer's voice will be really strong. It also helps if you pick a topic you care about. Here's a list of topic ideas. Pick one of these if you like it. Feel free to think of your own idea.

Some Writing Ideas

1. What I do for fun in the winter

2. The most important thing about my mom (dad, brother, sister)

3. Something I wish I could do

4. A bad fall

5. Something annoying

6. My idea _____

My topic will be _____.

Draw First

Think about your topic. What do you picture in your mind? What do you feel? Make your reader see and feel those things too. Use colored pencils or crayons to help you with the details. If you need more space, use another piece of paper.

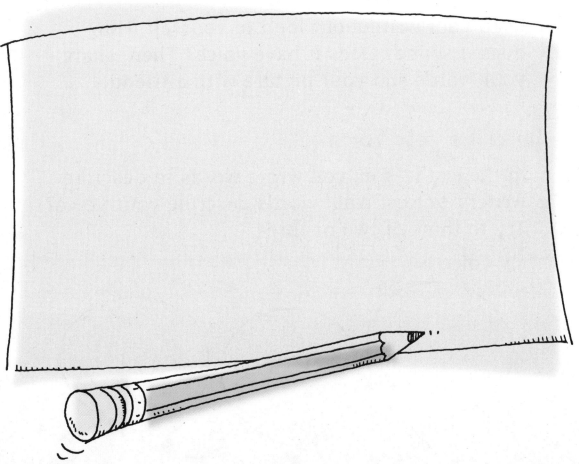

Write Next

What words and sentences would go with your picture? Don't try to tell everything. Readers like to hear the important details. They like to hear your voice. You can write here or you can write on the paper with your picture.

_____

_____

_____

_____

Share

Read your writing out loud to yourself. How does it sound? Does it have voice? Then, share your words and your picture with a friend.

Describe Your Voice

In the last lesson, you wrote words to describe writers' voices. What words describe your voice? Try to think of two or three.

My voice is

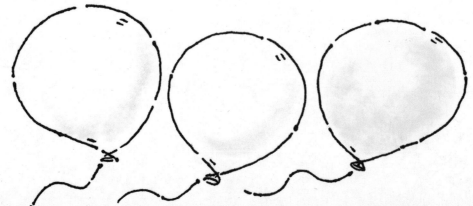

Scribbles Has a Question

"I don't know if my writing has any voice. How can I tell?"

How can you tell if writing has voice? What should we tell Scribbles?

A Writer's Secret

Describing words can add detail and voice to writing. These words are called adjectives. Read these two examples.

Before: The dog chased me. I saw his teeth.

After: The **snarling** dog chased me. I saw his **yellow** teeth.

Now you try. Help Scribbles with this sentence.

Before: I saw the boy get on the horse.

After: I saw the _____ boy get on the

_____ horse.

name: ....   date: ....

More Voice, Please!

Sometimes one piece of pizza is not enough. You want more! Some pieces of writing give you plenty of voice. Some leave you hungry. But there is one thing you can do. Put plenty of voice into your writing. That way, your readers will never go hungry!

Read

Reading out loud is the best way to hear and feel voice in writing. Read a short sample of writing out loud. The sample is written in two different ways. Which one gives you plenty of voice? Which one leaves you hungry for more?

Sample 1

A little boy was sitting in a train car. It was raining. There were two women in the car. He didn't know them. They talked and knitted a lot.

_____ Plenty of voice!

_____ I need more voice! I'm still hungry!

Sample 2

A little boy was sitting in the corner of a railway carriage looking out at the rain, which was splashing against the windows and blotching downward in an ugly, dirty way. He was not the only person in the carriage, but the others were strangers to him. He was alone as usual. There were two women opposite him, a fat one and a thin one, and they talked without stopping, smacking their lips in between sentences and seeming to enjoy what they said as much as if it were something to eat. They were knitting all the time, and whenever the train stopped the click-clack of their needles was loud and clear like two clocks.

L.M. Boston. *The Children of Green Knowe.* (Orlando: Harcourt, 1955), page 1.

____ Plenty of voice!

____ I need more voice! I'm still hungry!

Think and Share

Which sample did you like? Which one had more voice? Which one do you think the author really wrote?

Think and Revise

This writing needs your help. Read it out loud to yourself. Does it have enough voice?

Rainy days are fun. Some people don't like rainy days.

I think they are fun. There are lots of things to do on

a rainy day.

This writing needs more voice. Try one or more of these ideas. Check off each thing you try.

___ Change a boring word

___ Change another boring word

___ Add a detail (something you see or hear or smell)

___ Share your honest feelings about rainy days

___ Start one sentence a different way

___ Make one sentence a question

Share with a Partner

Take turns with your partner reading your work out loud. How does it sound? Do you want to add or change anything else?

Scribbles Has a Question

"Once I write something, I do not like to change it. Could one little, tiny change add any voice?"

What do you think? Can tiny changes make a difference?

A Writer's Secret

A strong writer's voice needs to tell the truth. Say what you really think and feel.

Here is what Juan wrote at first:

Our car trip was long. I had a good time.

Later, he wanted to share his real feelings:

Our car trip took forever! The car was hot, and my legs got cramped. Next time, I hope we can fly.

Which has more voice?

Word Choice

You are ready to watch TV. Wait—it's the same show you watched last night. The same show was on the night before that, too.

"Hey!" you scream. "I want a new show! I've heard all this before!"

Readers sometimes feel that way, too. They want new and interesting words. That's your job as a writer. You must give readers words they will love.

name: ....   date: ....

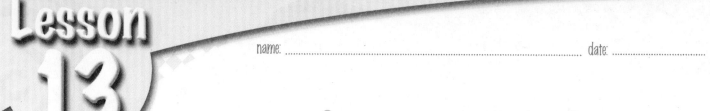

Not Again!

Think how hard it would be to write an interesting story with only 15 words. Boring! Believe it or not, some writers use only about 15 different words. We want you to use lots of words. After all, the world is filled with words!

Read

Read "The Scary Dog." The author may have used some words too many times. What do you think?

The Scary Dog

Our neighbors have a dog. He is a scary dog. He scares all the kids who walk by. I am scared of him. He makes scary sounds and jumps around in a scary way.

Think and Share

Talk about "The Scary Dog" with a friend. Which words are repeated too many times? Does the author create a clear or fuzzy picture of the dog?

Read and Think

Read this next story on your own two times. The first time, listen and watch for repeated words. The second time, use your pencil to circle those words.

A Really Nice Time

I had a really nice time at Jordan's house. His mom is really nice. We played this really nice game. Afterward, we had some really nice cookies for a snack.

Think and Revise

We thought the writer used the words "really nice" too many times. Do you agree? What are some other words the author could have used? Write your words in the spaces.

A Really Nice Time

I had a really nice time at Jordan's house. His mom

is _____. We played this _____ game.

Afterward, we had some _____ cookies for

a snack.

Share

Share your new words with a friend. Did your friend choose the same new words?

Write

Think about a fun time you had with a friend. Write 3–5 sentences about it. Try not to repeat important words. The more kinds of words you use, the clearer your ideas will be.

Share and Think

Read your sentences out loud to yourself. Did you use any words too many times? Share your sentences with a friend. Put a check in the blank that shows how you feel about your writing.

____ I used a lot of different words.

____ I used some words too many times.

Scribbles Has a Question

"I love pizza! I love peaches! I love green beans!"

"I love using my favorite words! I love repeating and repeating!"

What would you like to tell Scribbles about word choice?

_____

_____

_____

_____

A Writer's Secret

Writers who read a lot learn many new words. When you learn new words, you do not need to use the old ones as often. As you read, notice the words the author uses. Write down your favorites.

name: .... date: ....

Verb Power!

Verbs are like the engine in a car. An engine gets a car moving. A verb gets your sentence moving. Verbs show action: run, walk, whisper, talk. Some verbs have more power than others, just like some car engines. For example, which has more power?

The eagle moved.

The eagle soared.

Read

Read each pair of sentences on pages 57 and 58. The verbs are in color. Which verb gives the sentence more power? Circle it.

Sample 1

I went down the street.

I raced down the street.

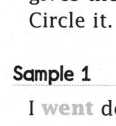

Sample 2

My brother **gobbled** his food like an animal.

My brother **ate** his food like an animal.

Sample 3

The announcer's voice **came** out of the loudspeaker.

The announcer's voice **boomed** out of the loudspeaker.

Share and Check

Check your work with a friend. Did you circle the same verbs?

Write

Write what a verb is.

_____

_____

_____

Write with Verbs

Think about recess. Picture yourself on the
playground or in the gym. What are you doing?
Write 2–3 sentences about it. Use strong verbs to
tell about your actions. Circle the verbs you use.
Put a little star by the strongest one.

_____

_____

_____

_____

_____

_____

_____

Scribbles Has a Question

"OK, I think I've got it. A verb is an action word. What verbs could I use to write about what I am doing?"

Help Scribbles think of some verbs he could use to write about himself. Make a list.

_____

_____

A Writer's Secret

Sometimes, writers go too fast! They might think about a word but forget to write it down. Always read over your writing when you are done. Then, your reader won't wonder what you mean.

Scribbles left a verb out of this sentence. What do you think he meant to say?

The cat on the chicken.

Use the Clues

What do you do when you see a hard word? Maybe you can say the word, but you don't know what it means. Have you ever tried making a guess using clues?

Read for New Words

In the sentence below, the author is talking about Dragon, a farmer's cat. The word in color might be new to you. As you read the word, try to guess what it means.

He had seven claws on each foot, and a thick, furry tail, which lashed angrily from side to side.

Robert C. O'Brien. *Mrs. Frisby and the Rats of NIMH.* (New York: Aladdin, 1971), p. 21.

What do you think *lashed* means?

_____

_____

_____

How did you figure out what
lashed means?

_____

_____

_____

_____

Lashed=whipped

Read and Think

Here is a passage from another book, *Ragweed*, by
Avi. Ragweed is a country mouse seeing a human
city for the first time. Use the clues to make good
guesses about what each word means. Write your
guesses in the space marked MY NOTES.

My Notes

As they went along Ragweed was able to gain
a better sense of Amperville—or at least the
section known as Mouse Town. It was too dark to
see much, he reminded himself, and the lights
on long poles were not very effective, but most
of what he saw appeared to be very rundown.
Human nests seemed abandoned. Windows
were broken. Doors were shattered. The wide,
dusty streets were littered with bits of paper,
metal, wood. Abandoned cars were everywhere.

Avi. *Ragweed*. (New York: HarperCollins, 1999), p. 50.

Drawing It Out

Sometimes drawing a picture can help you see what a word means. Use the spaces below to draw some pictures.

It was too dark to see, and the lights on poles were not **effective**. What might that look like?

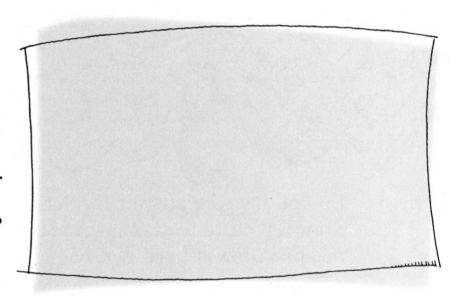

Everything looked **rundown**. Cars were **abandoned**, and the streets were **littered**.

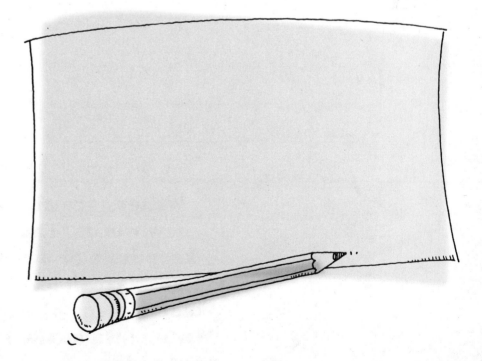

Scribbles Has a Question

"My name has a special meaning. Do you know what it means?"

Do you have an answer for Scribbles? Can you draw a picture to show what Scribbles's name means? Draw it here.

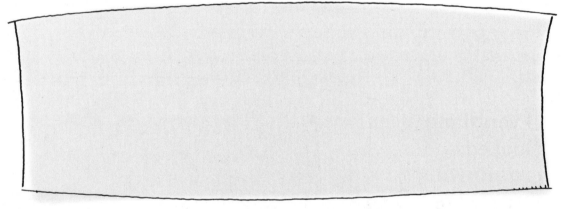

A Writer's Secret

Writers are always looking for new words. They even like to keep lists of new words they find. Next time you are reading, keep a piece of paper nearby. Write down some new words you want to learn.

name: .... date: ....

Tickling
the Senses

Words about seeing, tasting, hearing, smelling, and touching tickle a reader's senses. If you write about "a bowl of fluffy white, lightly buttered, freshly popped popcorn," your readers will hear the pop, smell the butter, and feel the crunch. This is a good way to get your readers' attention.

Read and Make Notes

First, get a pencil. Then, read a passage from *The Chocolate Touch*, by Patrick Skene Catling. In this book, everything John touches turns to chocolate. Underline any words that help you see, hear, smell, taste, or feel things.

John had been so busy feeling sorry for himself that he had not realized how his mother and father would feel about his chocolate disease. "Never mind, Mother," he said, putting his arm around her shoulders. "It's all right." Really, nothing was all right, he couldn't bear to see his mother's tears.

He kissed her wet cheek. His eyes were shut as his lips softly touched her, so he didn't see the change right away. Then his lips began to feel sticky. He opened his eyes. His mother had turned into a lifeless statue of chocolate!

Patrick Skene Catling. *The Chocolate Touch.* (New York: Bantam Doubleday Dell, 1952), p. 77.

Think and Write

Read through the passage one more time. Underline anything you missed the first time. Now, look at the chart below. Fill in each part with words you underlined.

I see	
I hear	
I touch	
I smell	
I taste	

Draw a Place

Think about a favorite place—the beach, a city park, a cozy room. Draw a picture of it. Use colors to help with details.

Things I See... Things I hear... Things I smell... Things I feel...

Things I taste... Things I see... Things I hear... Things I smell...

Write to Tickle

Now, put your picture into words and sentences. (Look at your chart again to remember how the author did it.) Try to write at least 3–5 sentences.

_____

_____

_____

_____

_____

Scribbles Has a Question

"How many senses are there? Let's see—oh, see! That's one. What else can you do besides see things?"

Scribbles is a bit out of touch with his senses. Help him out, please!

A Writer's Secret

When writers go back to revise their work, they don't always make big changes. Sometimes changing even one word can change the picture in a reader's mind. Look at this sentence:

Before: I really miss the **noise** of the waves against the beach.

After: I really miss the **crashing** of the waves against the beach.

Look back at the sentences you wrote about a place. Find one word to add or change.

Sentence Fluency

Have you ever watched fish swimming in a tank or in a lake? They move so gracefully. Now, think about writing. When words go together just right, they flow, too. The sound is easy on your ears. The word for that is **fluency**. In this unit, we'll talk about ways to put fluency into your writing.

name: _____ date: _____

Keep It Rolling

Have you ever seen a snowball roll downhill? As it goes, it gathers more snow. A good piece of writing should keep rolling along just like that snowball. Each sentence adds a little more detail. How many details do you need? You have to decide when your "snowball" is big enough.

Read

On the next page are two short samples. Read each one carefully. Decide which one is more interesting.

Sample 1

I like it when my dad and I don't walk straight home from school.

Sample 2

I like it when my dad and I don't walk straight home from school. If I don't have basketball practice or homework, we take our time. We collect leaves or hunt for caterpillars. Sometimes we go to the playground and shoot baskets. If I'm hungry, we might stop for ice cream. The one thing we don't do is hurry. Not hurrying is the part I love best!

Think and Share

Which one did you like better? Was it Sample 2? What did the writer do to make Sample 2 more interesting? Look at the list below. Put a star by any of the things you think the author did.

In Sample 2, the writer:

___ 1. Added details

___ 2. Kept the idea rolling along

___ 3. Shared feelings

___ 4. Made word pictures

Did we forget anything? Write it here:

_____

_____

Choose

In Sample 1, the writer started and then stopped. Look at this list of writing topics. Choose one or think of your own topic. Choose an idea that you can really keep rolling.

Writing ideas

1. A brave thing to do

2. Something interesting I found

3. A teacher you should meet

4. My own idea _____

My topic is _____ .

Think, Write, and Roll

Think about your topic. What do you want to say first? What details will keep it rolling along? When you feel ready, write at least 3 sentences about your topic. Write more if you can. Build your idea one detail at a time!

_____

_____

_____

_____

_____

Scribbles Has a Question

"After writing one sentence I felt tired. Is it OK to just stop? My reader won't mind."

What advice do you have for Scribbles?

_____

_____

A Writer's Secret

Writers know that you can't just put down a bunch of words and call it a sentence. What things does a *complete sentence* have? Check each one that is right:

____ a capital letter at the start

____ punctuation at the end **. ? !**

____ a complete thought

____ enough words to make sense

name: .... date: ....

Making Changes

Most people enjoy change. They do not want to do the very same things every single day. Surprises make life interesting. Readers like change, too. They don't want every single sentence to begin the same way.

Read

Read "At My School" out loud. That way you can hear the writing better.

At My School

At my school we have fun. At my school we have nice teachers. At my school we have a new playground. At my school we have a garden with flowers and vegetables. At my school we have a big library.

How did you like "At My School"? Put an **X** in the right blank.

___ I want to hear more!

___ Ouch! Thank goodness it ended.

Revise

This writer needs to revise, and you can help. All you need to do is write one sentence a different way. Here is the first sentence:

Before: At my school we have fun.

After: My school is a great place.

See how the beginning changed? The writer used some different words, but the idea stayed the same. Now you try. We numbered the sentences for you. Pick any sentence *except Sentence 1*. Underline the sentence.

At My School

(1) At my school we have fun. (2) At my school we have nice teachers. (3) At my school we have a new playground. (4) At my school we have a garden with flowers and vegetables. (5) At my school we have a big library.

Now, write the sentence a different way but keep the idea the same:

_____

_____

_____

Write

Write your own paragraph, about 3–5 sentences long. Tell something interesting about your school. Make every sentence begin in a different way.

_____

_____

_____

_____

_____

_____

Think

After you write your paragraph, underline the first 3 words of every sentence. Look carefully at what you underlined. Does every sentence begin in a different way? Do you need to make any changes?

Scribbles Has a Question

"Let me read you my paper about dogs. It goes like this—
Dogs are fun. Dogs are cool. Dogs are neat. Dogs are our good friends! How do you like it?"

Scribbles seems to be stuck in a rut. All his sentences sound the same! How can we help him without hurting his feelings?

_____

_____

_____

A Writer's Secret

If you really want to hear if your writing is rolling along and has different sentence beginnings, read it out loud. You can read to yourself or a friend. Always have a pencil ready, so you can make changes if you need to.

Come On, Let's Hear It!

Some writing almost begs to be read out loud. The words flow along like the rhythm in a song. Writing like this is easy to read with expression, and it's fun for the listener, too. Reading out loud is a great way to test the fluency in writing. When the writing is choppy, reading out loud sounds choppy. When it's smooth, reading out loud is smooth and fun.

Read

Read out loud to yourself or with a partner. Compare these two passages from a book called *Muncha! Muncha! Muncha!* One passage is just the way the author really wrote it. One is not. See if you can hear and feel the difference.

Example 1

For years, Mr. McGreely dreamed. He dreamed of a garden. He would plant one. He thought of his hands. They would get dirty. He thought of vegetables. He would grow some. He would eat them. He would gobble them.

Example 2

For years, Mr. McGreely dreamed of planting a garden. He dreamed of getting his hands dirty, of growing yummy vegetables, and of gobbling them all up. But he never tried it until—"This spring!" said Mr. McGreely. "This spring, by golly, I'm going to plant a garden." So he hoed. And he sowed. And he watched his garden grow. Lettuce! Carrots! Peas! Tomatoes! "Yum! Yum! Yummy!" said Mr. McGreely. "I'll soon fill my tummy with crisp, fresh veggies."

Candace Fleming. *Muncha! Muncha! Muncha!* (New York: Atheneum, 2002).

Think

Did you hear a difference when you read the two versions? Could you feel the energy flowing in one passage more than the other? What do you think? Can you read with that same kind of energy and life? (You can!)

Read

Work with two or three classmates to read aloud the poem. First, read through the entire poem. Then, practice the line you will read.

Little Drops of Water
by Mother Goose

Little drops of water, [Line 1]

Little grains of sand, [Line 2]

Make the mighty ocean, [Line 3]

And the pleasant land. [Line 4]

Write

Create your own poem about summer. Keep it short, like the one you read. It could be about people, places, food, fun. (Your poem does not have to rhyme. Not all poetry does!)

_____

_____

_____

_____

Scribbles Has a Question

"Don't tell anyone, but I am very shy! Is it OK for me to read out loud?"

You might be shy sometimes, too. Share your feelings with Scribbles about reading out loud.

A Writer's Secret

We talked before about making sentence beginnings different. Well, good writers also think about sentence length. Some sentences can be short. Other sentences can be long. If they aren't, writing can sound like this:

I have a dog. My dog is nice. She likes to run. She can run fast.

What could this writer do next time?

name: .... date: ....

Math— a Big PLUS for Writing

Math is about numbers. Writing is all about words and ideas, right? Sometimes, a math idea can help you with your writing. You know how two smaller numbers make one bigger number? Well, instead of numbers, you use sentences. You put two (or three) smaller sentences together to make a bigger one.

I like cats. ✚ I like dogs. ＝

Read

Read a sample of writing. Look carefully. Does it flow smoothly or is it choppy?

My dad built a fence. My dad built a playhouse. My dad built a tool shed.

___ **Smooth**   ___ **Choppy**

The sentences are choppy, but they could go together. They are all about Dad. Let's try combining the ideas the way you add numbers:

My dad **built** a fence.

+

My dad **built** a playhouse.

+

My dad **built** a tool shed.

─────────────────────────────

= *My dad **built** a fence, a playhouse, and a tool shed.*

Read, Think, and Write

Now, you try. Read another sample of writing that could use some sentence combining.

My sister has a fish. His name is Sparkle.

Can you combine these two sentences? Write your big sentence here:

_____

_____

_____

Think and Write Again

Let's try again. Here are two more little sentences:

Sparkle is blue. Sparkle has black fins.

Can you combine these two sentences? Write your big sentence here:

_____

_____

_____

1 + 1 + 1 + 1 = ONE BIG SENTENCE!

You have added two sentences to make one. Do you think you could add four sentences? Try it. It's OK to start over if you get stuck. Here are four sentences about Sparkle the fish. See if you can put them all into one big sentence.

My sister has a fish.

His name is Sparkle.

Sparkle is blue.

Sparkle has black fins.

My big sentence:

_____

_____

_____

name: .... date: ....

Scribbles Has a Question

"I love cats. They have soft feet. Hey, could I put those two sentences together?"

Help Scribbles combine his sentences.

_____

_____

_____

A Writer's Secret

When good readers read out loud, their faces might show feelings. Their hands might move a little as they speak. Moving sometimes helps people read with more expression. Next time you hear someone read out loud, watch to see how the person shows feelings.

Conventions

Editing = Fixing the <u>Conventions</u>

When you clean up your room, you probably pick things up off the floor. Sometimes, you need to clean up your writing, too.

When it comes to good editing, timing is also important. You wouldn't vacuum before you picked up everything off the floor. So, think and write first. Then, put on your editor's hat to look for mistakes. These things are called **conventions**. Editing—fixing the conventions—is how you clean up your writing.

name: .... date: ....

Telling or Asking?

When you talk with friends, how do you know when they are asking you something (question) or telling you something (statement)? Listening helps. The speaker's voice gives you a clue. In writing, the "clues" are special words or punctuation marks writers use to help readers know when they are telling or asking.

Question or Statement?

Use your ears to decide which sentences are questions and which are statements. Circle the right word for each one.

1. The cold wind made me button my jacket

   Question   **Statement**

2. May I go to Trevor's house

   Question   **Statement**

3. Why didn't you pick up
   your room

   Question   Statement

4. I can't find my basketball
   shoes

   Question   Statement

5. If you had a million
   dollars, what would you
   do with it

   Question   Statement

Think

Put a question mark (?) if you circled question and a period (.) if you circled statement. If you are not sure, read the sentence again.

Read & Respond

Read this short paragraph. Fill in a period (.) or a question mark (?) for each sentence. Read the sentences out loud if you are not sure.

Sharing Can Be Hard

I took my new remote control car over to my friend's

house   He has a brother Jon who is four and a

brother Kyle who is two   Can you guess what

happened   Yes, they all wanted a turn with my car

Who do you think wanted to go first   If you guessed

Jon, you are correct   He wanted to drive it all day

Write

Write a 3–5 sentence paragraph about a time you shared something. At least one of your sentences needs to be a question. Don't forget to put in periods for your statements and question marks for your questions.

_____

_____

_____

_____

_____

_____

_____

_____

Scribbles Has a Question

"What if I am reading to myself? Can I still hear if a sentence is a question?"

Do you have to hear sentences read out loud to know if they are questions?

A Writer's Secret

"Look both ways before crossing a street." This safety tip can help you with your writing. When writers edit, they look "both ways" for each sentence, checking for important things like capital letters and ending punctuation. When you edit, look at both ends of your sentences to make sure they have what they need.

name: .... date: ....

Tools of the Trade

When you clean your room, you might use tools like a vacuum cleaner or a dust cloth. Editors use tools like pencils. They also use special symbols. Each symbol sends a message, like a code, that tells how to fix the writing.

No Crowding!

Did you ever get too close to someone in line? Did you feel squashed? People need space. Words need space, too. If they get bunched up together, they can be hard to read. Read this sample sentence to yourself.

I had a really funnydream last night.

Did any of those words look crowded? Here's the symbol an editor uses to show a space is needed:

I had a really funny#dream last night.

The message is "Put a space here." It is also important for the editor to put the symbol right where the space is needed. Practice writing the symbol in the right place: funnydream

Warm Up

Let's try out our new symbol. Here are 3 sentences for you to read. Have your pencil ready to help you edit. Use the # symbol to say, "Put a space here."

1. I forgot to turn the computeroff.

2. May Ihave a little more?

3. Myteam has practice onTuesday.

Practice

Here's a short paragraph that needs your editing help. Use the # symbol to show where space is needed. (HINT: Some writers might crowd more than just two words together.)

My friend Gracie spentthe night on Friday. She brought a moviefor us to watch. It is toorainy for us to play intheyard. We get to order a pizzaand make cookies, too.

I used the ⚓ symbol _____ times.

Share with a Friend

Meet with a friend and compare your editing work. Did you find the same number of spacing errors? Check the paragraph with your class. Be ready to share your comments and questions.

Scribbles Has a Question

"Whydoweneedspaces betweenourwords?"

As a writer and an editor, what do you think? What is the big deal about spaces between words?

_____

_____

_____

A Writer's Secret

When you write, be sure you write on every other line. That way, it will be easier to spot mistakes. Also, if you need to edit something, you will have plenty of room!

name: .... date: ....

Capitals at the Start

Every sentence needs to start with a capital letter. Sometimes though writers forget. A good editor will spot this error and mark it, so the reader will not get confused. Remember, editors have their own special code. They use symbols. This symbol ≡ means, "Hey, this letter needs to be a capital!"

Read Like an Editor

Are you reading like an editor? Read these sample sentences to yourself. Watch out for missing capital letters.

It's my job to rake the leaves. every tree in our yard has dropped its leaves except for the big one in the front. Hurry up, tree!

What did you notice? The second sentence does not begin with a capital letter. Here's how the editor would use the symbol ≡ to show a capital is needed:

It's my job to rake the leaves. e̲very tree in our yard has dropped its leaves except for the big one in the front. Hurry up, tree!

Warm Up

Here are some warm up sentences for you to read and edit. Put the ≡ symbol under each letter that should be a capital.

1. when will dinner be ready?

2. If it snows hard, we won't have school. we can play.

3. swimming is my favorite sport. we have a pool in our neighborhood.

How many times did you use the ≡ symbol?

I used it _____ times.

Practice

Here's a paragraph in need of a sharp-eyed editor. Watch out for missing capital letters. Use the ≡ symbol to let the writer know what needs to be done. (**HINT:** Do you remember the symbol that says, "Put a space here"? There might be a spacing problem or two in this paragraph.)

walking in the rain is a lot of fun. it's even more fun when there are lots of puddles. I wear boots so I canjump in every puddle. the deep puddles are thebest.

I used the ≡ symbol _____ times.

I used the ⨥ symbol _____ times.

Share with a Friend

Did your editing go smoothly? Meet with a friend to compare your editing work. Did you find the same number of missing capital letters? How about spacing errors?

Scribbles Has a Question

"I have capital letters on most of my sentences. That's good enough, isn't it?"

As a reader, what would you like to tell Scribbles about capital letters?

A Writer's Secret

Being a good editor takes practice. When you help edit the work of other writers, it will help your own writing, too. You will begin to look at your own work with a sharper eye. You may even begin to catch yourself before you make some mistakes.

name: .... date: ....

I Know It on Sight!

When you see someone often, you soon know that person "by sight." Some words you see and use all the time, too. After a while, you know them by sight. If they are spelled wrong, you can tell.

Read

Here is a list of words. You know them well. We put each word in a sentence so it's easy to see how it could fit in your own writing.

they   I think **they** left without me!

you   Will **you** get my coat?

for   Wait **for** me by the door, please.

are   What **are** you doing?

with   I will go **with** you.

have   We **have** a dog.

one   She only took **one**.

like   I **like** that kind of music.

Warm Up

Here are some sentences that need your help. Read each sentence carefully. Watch out for sight words from the list. Draw a line through each word that is spelled wrong, like this:

~~thay~~

Then, write the correct spelling in the space above the word, like this

they
~~thay~~

I am going to a play today whith my parents. Thay say I hav to dress up. Do yuw lik plays?

Practice

Fix the words that are spelled wrong.

Big brothers aer a pain. I hav two of them, and only wun is nice. I liek both of them, but only one at a time. Do you have eny brothers?

Change Hats

It's time to change hats from editor to writer. Choose your own topic or pick one of these:

___ A brother or sister

___ Being an editor

___ A scary time on a bike!

My own topic: _____

Write

Write a short poem or paragraph about your topic. Use at least five of the words from the list on page 100. (You may use any of the words more than once!)

_____

_____

_____

_____

Scribbles Has a Question

"I have tons of imagination. Why can't I make up my own spelling? Is that a good idea?"

What advice do you have for Scribbles? What should you do when you are not sure how to spell a word?

A Writer's Secret

Write first—then edit. If you try to edit while you write, it is like putting your shoes on before your socks! It does not work very well! First, you need to get your ideas on paper. Then, go back to check for spacing, spelling, and punctuation.

Wrap-up Activity 1

Which Trait Is It?

You have studied six traits now. Can you remember all six? Here is a list (just in case).

- Ideas
- Organization
- Voice
- Word Choice
- Sentence Fluency
- Conventions

Now, let's look at some ways to describe each trait. Read each one. Then, mark the right blank to show which trait is described.

1. This trait is about strong sentences. When you use this trait well, your sentences are smooth and easy to read out loud. This trait is called

___ Word Choice   ___ Sentence Fluency   ___ Ideas

2. This trait is about choosing just the right word to say what you mean. It is called

___ Conventions   ___ Organization   ___ Word Choice

3. This trait is about correct spelling and punctuation. It is called

___ Ideas   ___ Convention   ___ Voice

4. If you use this trait well, your writing will have a strong main idea and interesting details. This trait is called

___ Ideas   ___ Word Choice   ___ Conventions

5. When you use this trait well, everything is in order. Your writing is easy to follow. This trait is called

___ Conventions   ___ Word Choice   ___ Organization

6. This trait makes your writing sound just like you. It makes your writing lively. This trait is called

___ Conventions   ___ Voice   ___ Organization

Wrap-up Activity 2

Writing Detective

Read each sample. Then, mark the right blank to show the problem you found.

Sample 1

I like my cat. I like my dog. I like school. I like lots of things. I like my friends.

The problem in Sample 1 is the

——— Word Choice: The writer's words are not clear.

——— Fluency: The writer begins every sentence the same way.

——— Conventions: A lot of the words are spelled wrong.

Sample 2

i love ise cream it is my favorite thing to eat i could eet it for every meal.

The problem in Sample 2 is the

——— Ideas: The writer's message is not clear.

——— Voice: The writer doesn't seem to like ice cream very much.

——— Conventions: The writing has mistakes.

Sample 3

My Uncle Bert came to visit. We went camping. I have a new pet turtle. Her name is Ollie.

The problem in Sample 3 is the

——— Conventions: Words are spelled wrong and the writer forgot periods.

——— Ideas: The writer is talking about two different topics.

——— Fluency: All the sentences begin the same way.

Wrap-up Activity 3

Dear Scribbles

Scribbles is worried. He is trying to write a story, but he is having trouble. He is worried that his writing isn't very good. He needs help.

You know a lot about writing. Maybe you can help. Write Scribbles a note. Give him some ideas on how to do his very best writing.

Dear Scribbles,

_____

_____

_____

_____

_____